# Useful Energy

## 1 Energy is Work

- **Energy** is **work** that **has been** done or work that **is able** to be done.

- For any **work** (or job) to happen, **energy** has to be **given**.

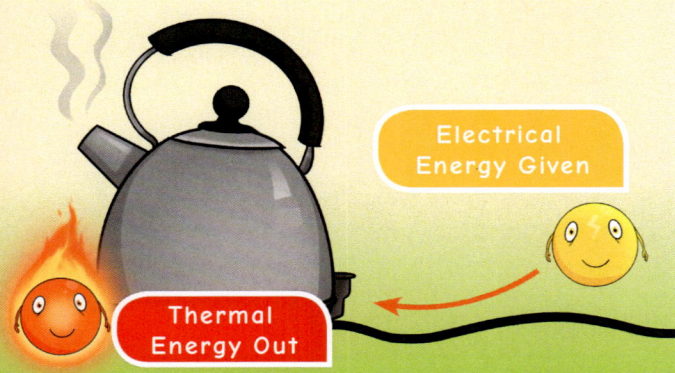

Electrical Energy Given

Thermal Energy Out

## 2 Job = Activity

A 'job' can be any activity:

- A person **eating**.

- A lorry **moving**.

- A kettle **boiling**.

- A TV **working**.

## 3 Joules (j)

- The **size** of the **job** is the **work done**.

- **Work** is measured in **joules** (j).

Work is measured in joules (j)

## 4 Energy = Work

The **more energy** supplied, the **more work** can be done.

- The faster you run, the **more** energy you need.

- The **higher** you jump, the **more** energy you need.

- The **more** soil you move, the **more** energy you need.

# Forms of Energy

## Chemical Energy

During a chemical change, energy is released.

## Sound Energy

- When particles vibrate they give out energy in the form of sound waves.

- Sound waves travel through liquids, solids and gases.

- They do <u>not</u> travel through a vacuum.

## Kinetic Energy (KE)

- Anything moving has kinetic energy.

- The kinetic energy in a body depends upon:
The mass (m) of the moving object.
The speed (v) of the moving object.

## Thermal Energy (or heat energy)

- Everything is made of molecules.

- These are always moving so they have kinetic energy.

**KS3 ONLY:**
- The total of all the KE in a substance is called the internal energy.

- The form of energy that makes the internal energy increase is called thermal energy (or heat energy).

## Light Energy

- Energy from the Sun is transferred by waves.

- Light waves are a type of electromagnetic wave.

- They are energy that we can see.

## Electrical Energy

- Electric currents move energy.

- When things are moved, work has been done so we know energy has been used.

- Electrical energy is used to make things happen.

## Potential Energy (PE)

- This is energy that something has because of its position or condition.

- It is the work that is **able to be done.**

## Gravitational Potential Energy (GPE)

GPE depends upon:

- The mass (m) of the body.

- The vertical height (h) it can fall through.

- The force of gravity (g) acting on it.

Example: A large skydiver has more GPE than a smaller person.

## Elastic Potential Energy

- The more strain you put on a spring, the more energy it will gain.

- The more turns you make on a wind up toy, the faster or further it will go.

# Transforming Energy

## 5   Energy Transformation

- Energy is **never** used up. It just **changes** from one form to another.

- This makes the energy **useful**.

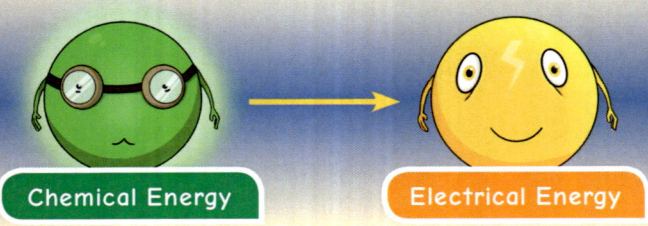

Chemical Energy → Electrical Energy

- Conservation of energy:
**Total amount of energy at the start = Total amount of energy at the end.**

## 6   Energy Transformation

- Energy in sunlight can be **changed** into electrical energy.

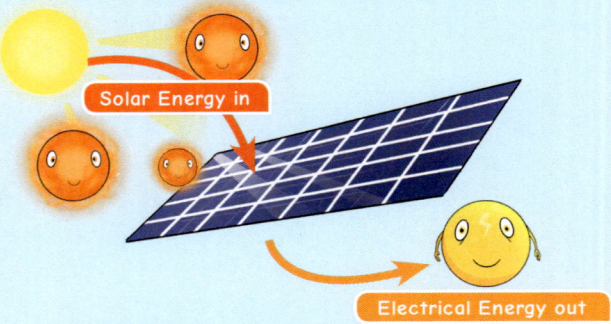

Solar Energy in

Electrical Energy out

- A lamp **changes** electrical energy into heat and light.

BUT when we change energy from one form to another, some energy is <u>useful</u> and some is <u>wasted</u>.

## 7   Energy Chain

- **Energy chains** show how energy is **transferred**.

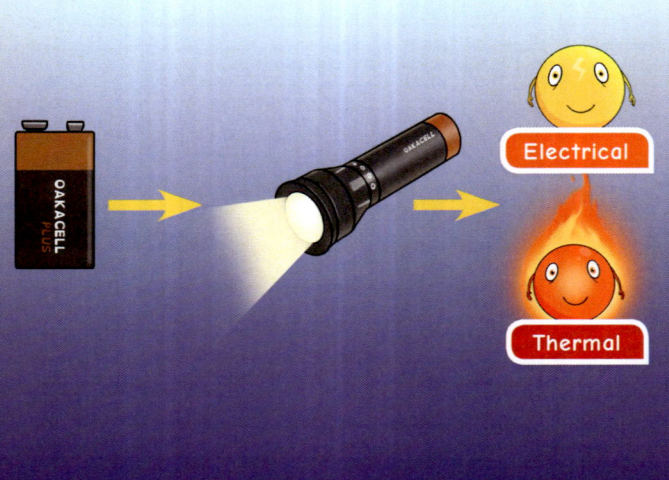

Electrical

Thermal

## 8   Thermal Energy Wasted

- **Thermal** energy (heat) is always **released**. This is usually **wasted** energy.

Why do I keep getting wasted?

# Transforming Energy

## 9   Elastic Potential Energy

- Wind up cars use a spring to **power** them.

- The spring stores **elastic potential energy.**

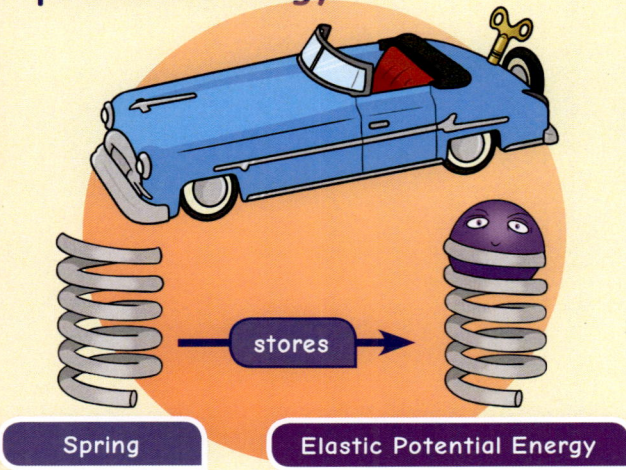

Spring — stores → Elastic Potential Energy

## 10   Transforming Energy

- As we wind up the car, we **transform kinetic energy** into elastic potential energy.

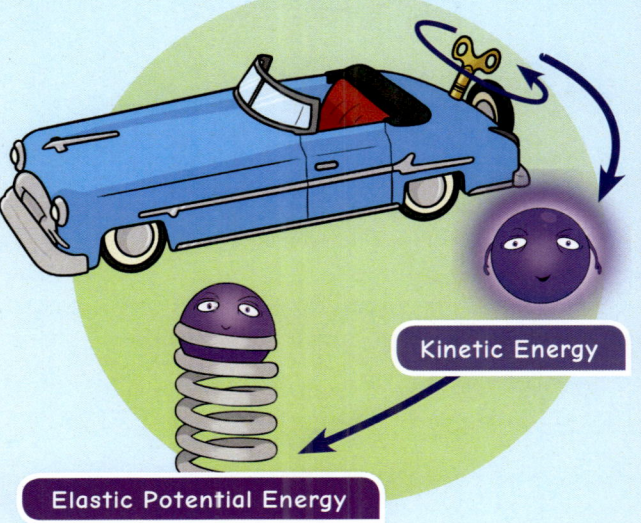

Kinetic Energy

Elastic Potential Energy

## 11   Transforming Energy

- The car then uses the **elastic potential energy** and **transforms** it into **kinetic energy.**

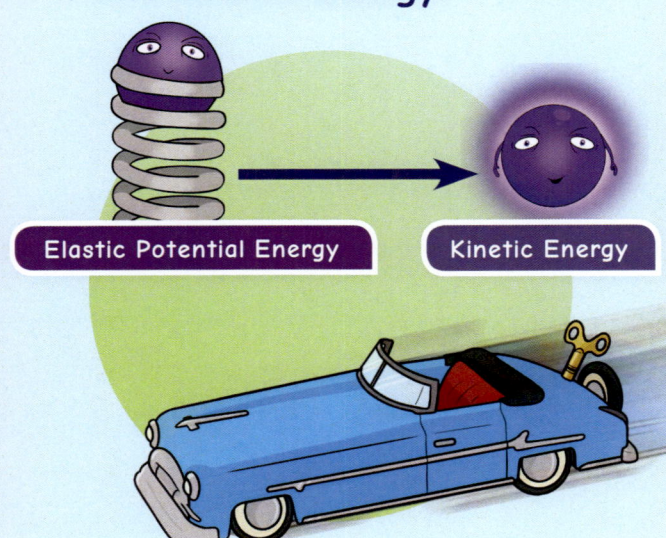

Elastic Potential Energy — Kinetic Energy

## 12   Electrical Energy

- **Electrical energy** is a very useful form of **energy.**

# Transforming Energy

## 13   Electrical Energy

- **Electrical energy** can be **transformed** to many different forms of **energy**.

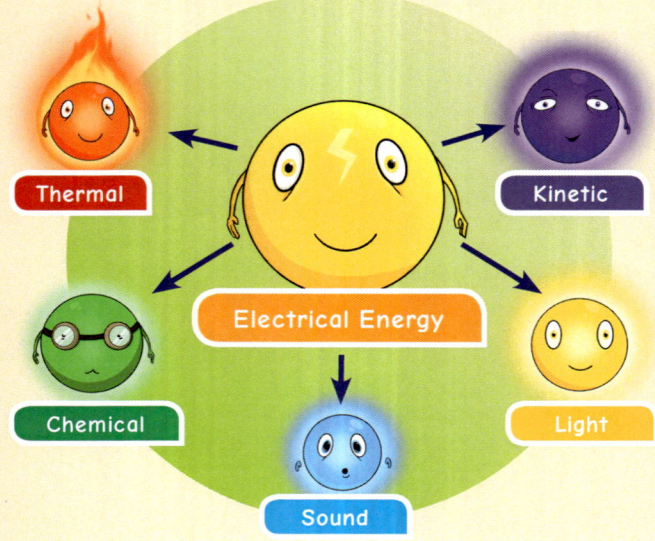

Thermal — Kinetic — Electrical Energy — Chemical — Light — Sound

## 14   A Television

- A TV set **transforms electrical energy** into **sound** and **light energy**.

Electrical — Sound — Light — Thermal

## 15   A Washing Machine

- A washing machine **transforms electical energy** into **thermal**, **sound** and **kinetic energy**.

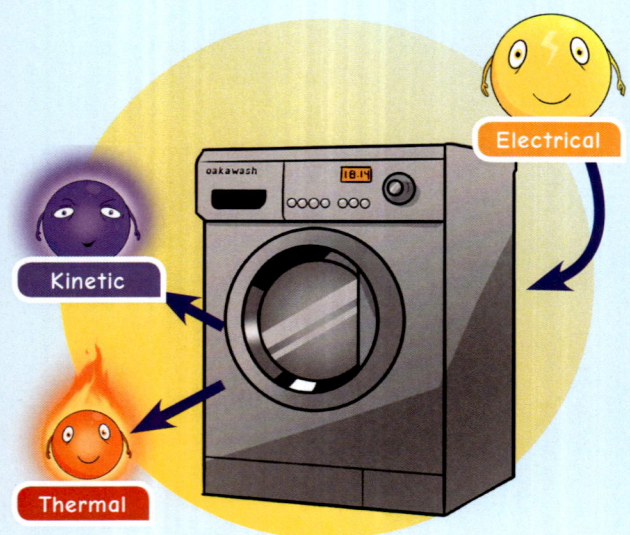

Electrical — Kinetic — Thermal

## 16   Storing Energy

- **Energy** can be stored.

- The stored **energy** in **fuels** is called **chemical** energy.

- **Batteries** are an example of stored **chemical energy**.

OAKACELL PLUS — Chemical Energy

# Useful Energy

## 17 Potential Energy

- Springs store **potential energy**.

- **Flywheels** (in machines) store **rotational energy. (KS3 ONLY)**

## 18 Wasted Energy

- When **energy** is **transformed**, from one form to another, not all of the **energy transformation** is useful.

- Some energy is **wasted**.

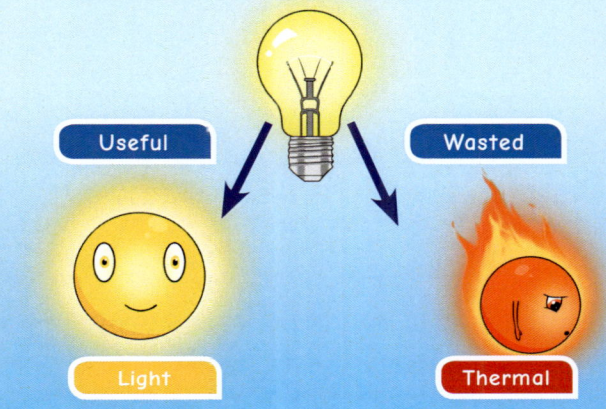

## 19 Useful & Wasted Energy from Food

- We **transform** the **chemical energy** in our food into **kinetic energy**.

- Some of the **chemical energy** in our food is **transformed** as **heat energy**.

- We need **energy** for **life processes** like movement.

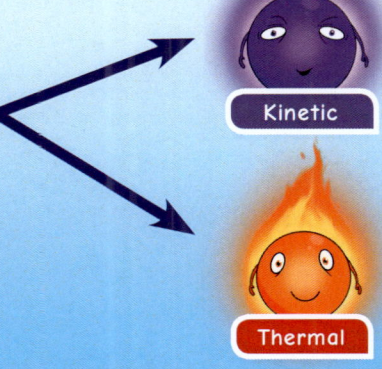

# Useful Energy from Food

## 20     Food Experiment

- The **intake** of energy (from food) should balance the **use** of energy (for life processes).

- The **amount of energy** in food is given in **joules or kilojoules**.

- We can measure the **amount of energy** in different foods by **burning** a food sample.

- The energy in the food is used to **raise the temperature of the water** in a test tube.

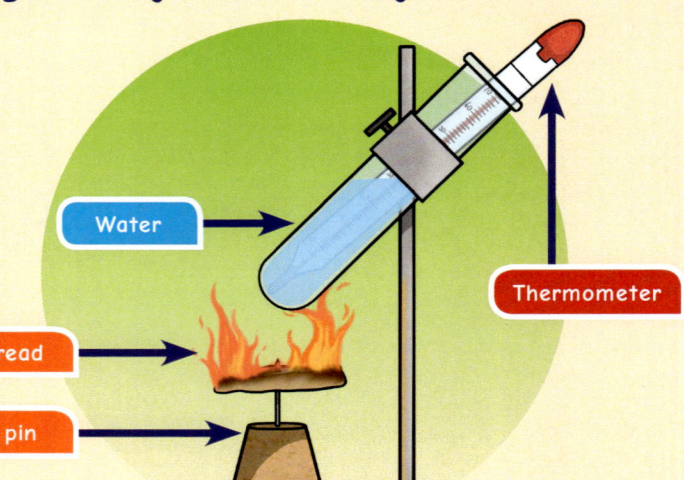

Water

Thermometer

Burning bread

Cork and pin

## 21     Dependent Variable

- Measure the temperature of the water before you start each test.

- Measure the water temperature at the end of each test.

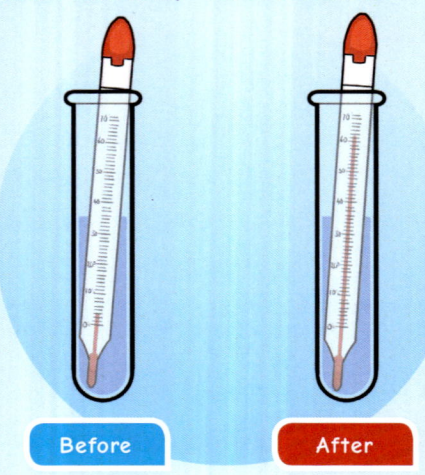

Before     After

## 22     Independent Variables

- Make sure you use the **same amount** (g) of each food type.

- Make sure you use the **same amount** of water for each test.

Always use the same amount!

- It takes **4.2J** to make the **temperature of 1cm³ of water rise by 1°C.**

# Sankey Diagrams

## 23   Sankey Diagram: Bicycle

- We can use **Sankey diagrams** to show the **energy** transfers.

- When we cycle, the **'energy in'** is **chemical energy** from the **food** we eat.

- The **'useful energy out'** is **kinetic energy** (movement energy) making the wheels go round.

- The **wasted energy** is **thermal energy**.

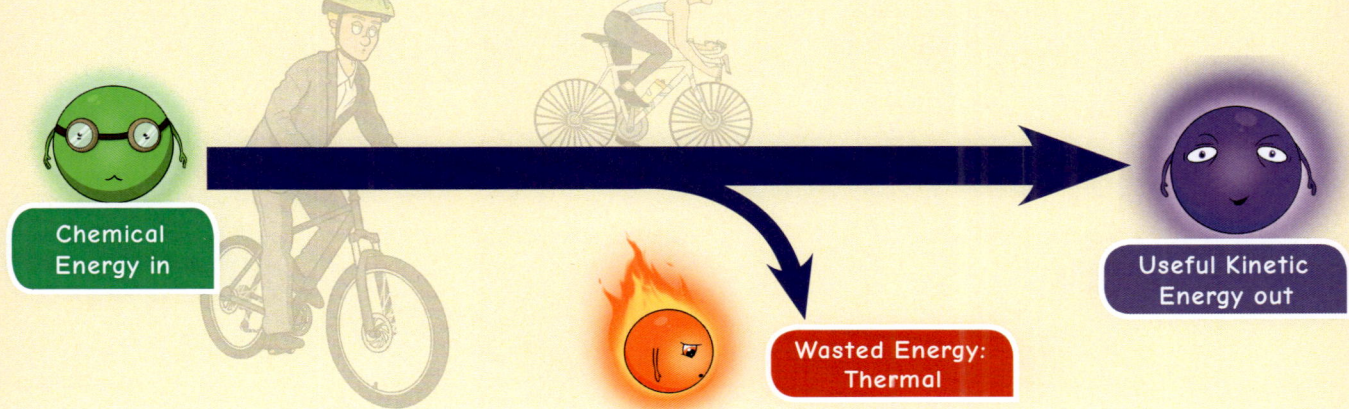

Chemical Energy in

Wasted Energy: Thermal

Useful Kinetic Energy out

## 24   Sankey Diagram: Filament Lamp

- If we measure the **useful energy out** and the total **energy in** we can **work out** the **percentage efficiency**.

- The **higher** the percentage **efficiency**, the **less** energy is **wasted**.

Energy Input: 20 Squares

Useful Energy output: 6 Squares

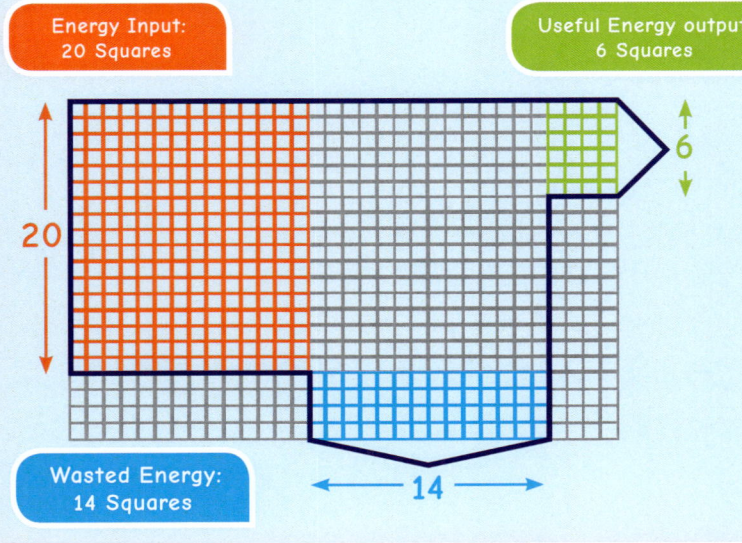

20

6

Wasted Energy: 14 Squares

14

How to find the percentage efficiency:

$$\% \text{ efficiency} = \frac{\text{Useful energy out}}{\text{Total energy in}} \times 100$$

$$\frac{6 \text{ Squares}}{20 \text{ Squares}} \times 100 = 30\% \text{ efficiency}$$

# Useful & Wasted Energy

**25** Useful and Wasted Energy

- Let's look at the **useful** and **wasted energy** in each of these devices.

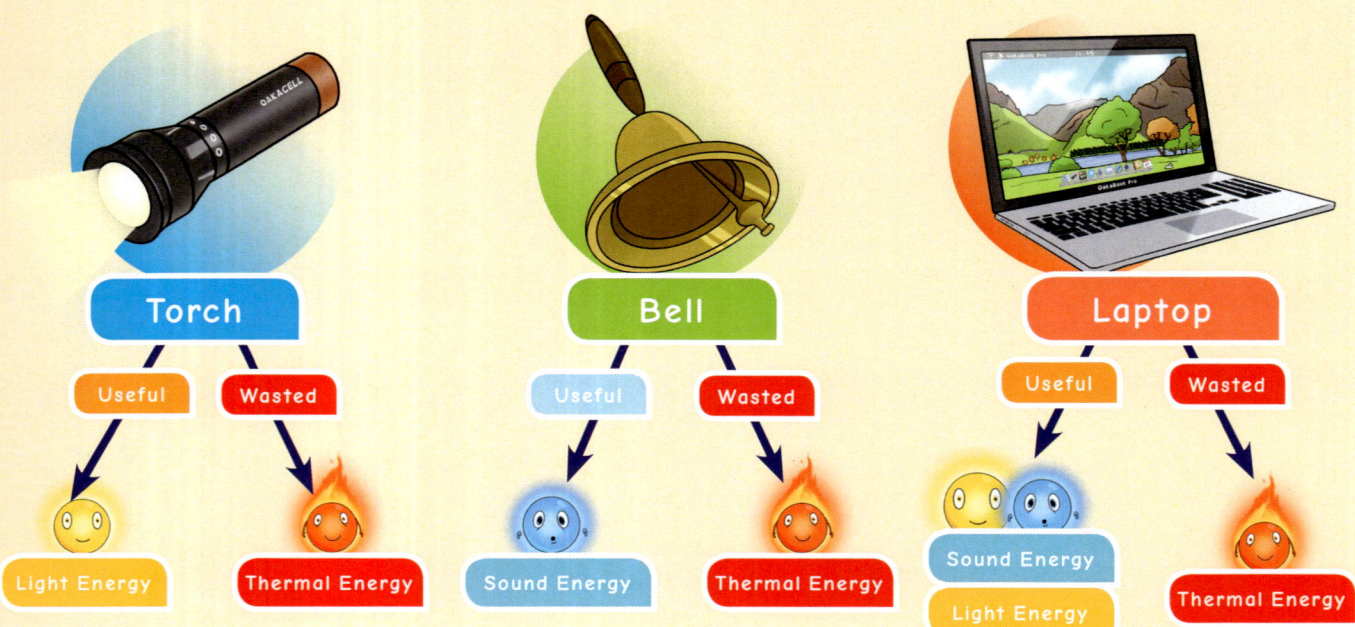

| Torch | Bell | Laptop |
|---|---|---|
| **Useful** — Light Energy / **Wasted** — Thermal Energy | **Useful** — Sound Energy / **Wasted** — Thermal Energy | **Useful** — Sound Energy, Light Energy / **Wasted** — Thermal Energy |

**26** Sankey Diagram: Torch

- The **useful energy** from a torch is **light energy**.

Chemical → Electrical → Light / Thermal

Chemical Energy in — Electrical — Useful Energy: Light

Wasted Energy: Thermal

- The **wasted energy** is **thermal energy**.

# Useful Energy

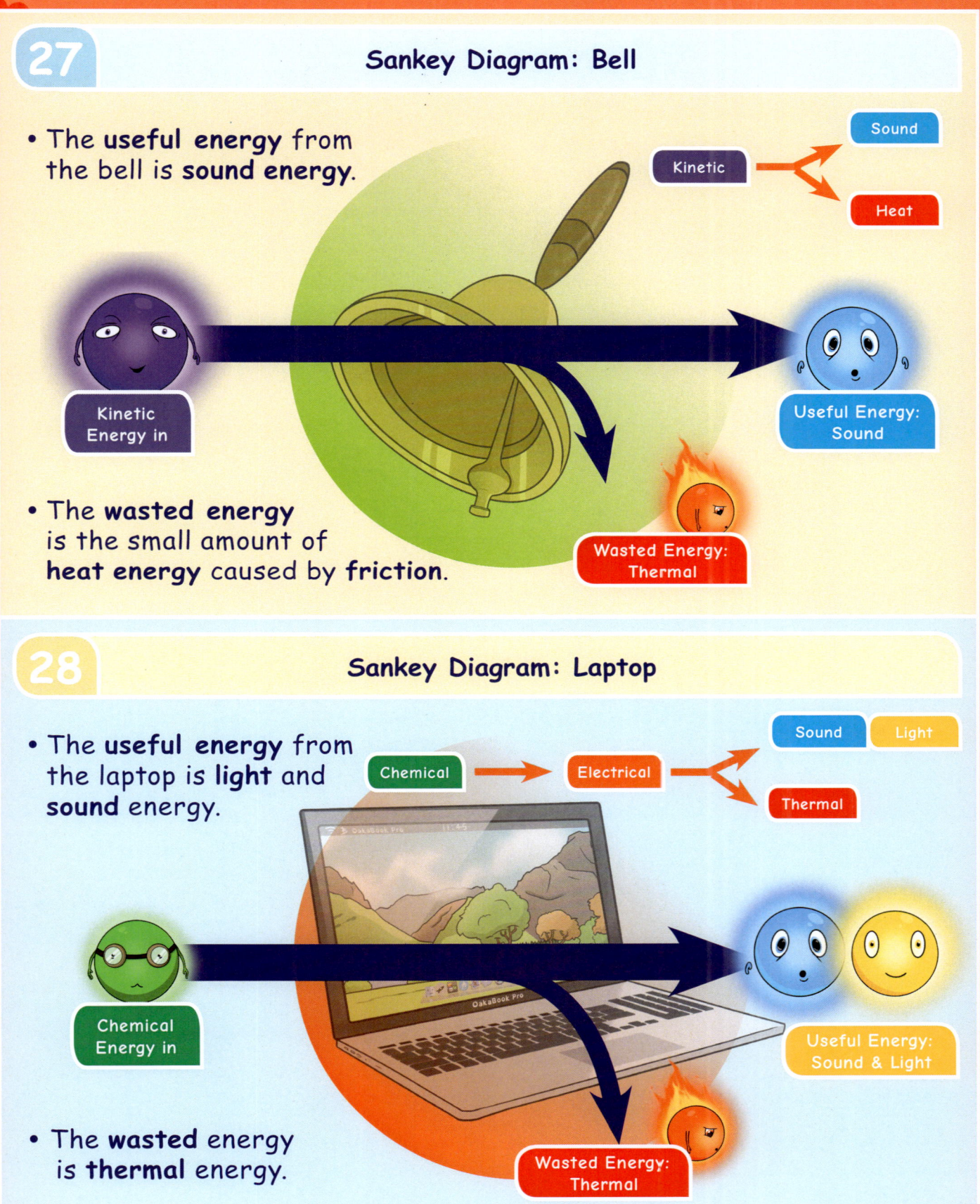

**27** Sankey Diagram: Bell

- The **useful energy** from the bell is **sound energy**.

Kinetic → Sound

Heat

Kinetic Energy in

Useful Energy: Sound

- The **wasted energy** is the small amount of **heat energy** caused by **friction**.

Wasted Energy: Thermal

**28** Sankey Diagram: Laptop

- The **useful energy** from the laptop is **light** and **sound** energy.

Chemical → Electrical → Sound Light

Thermal

Chemical Energy in

Useful Energy: Sound & Light

- The **wasted** energy is **thermal** energy.

Wasted Energy: Thermal

# Saving Energy
### (not tested for CE)

## 29    Energy Saving Bulbs

- We can save energy by using more **efficient** devices.

- **Energy** saving lamps are much more **efficient** than **filament** lamps.

- Energy saving lamps use much **less** electricity.

- They waste much **less** electricity than **thermal**.

- **LED** lamps are the most **efficient**.

**Filament Lightbulb**

## 40W
Life Expectancy: 1 Year

**Energy Saving Lightbulb**

## 11W
Life Expectancy: 6 - 10 Years

### KEY:

| | |
|---|---|
| Roof | 25% |
| Walls | 35% |
| Door | 15% |
| Windows | 10% |
| Floor | 15% |

## 30    Heat Loss in Buildings

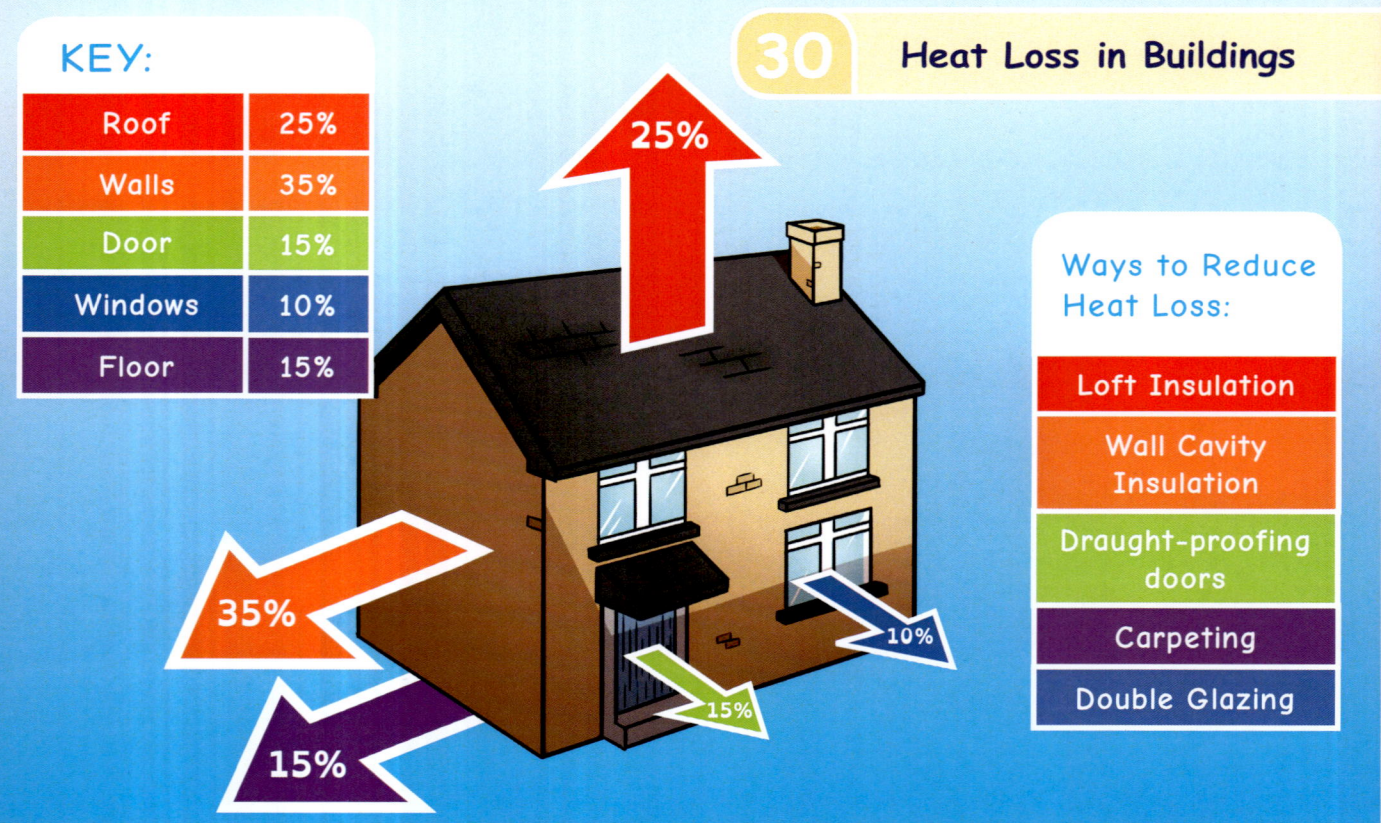

**Ways to Reduce Heat Loss:**

- Loft Insulation
- Wall Cavity Insulation
- Draught-proofing doors
- Carpeting
- Double Glazing

# Useful Energy

## 31 High Emission Energy

- **Power stations** transfer chemical, nuclear, solar, heat and kinetic energy into **electrical energy**.

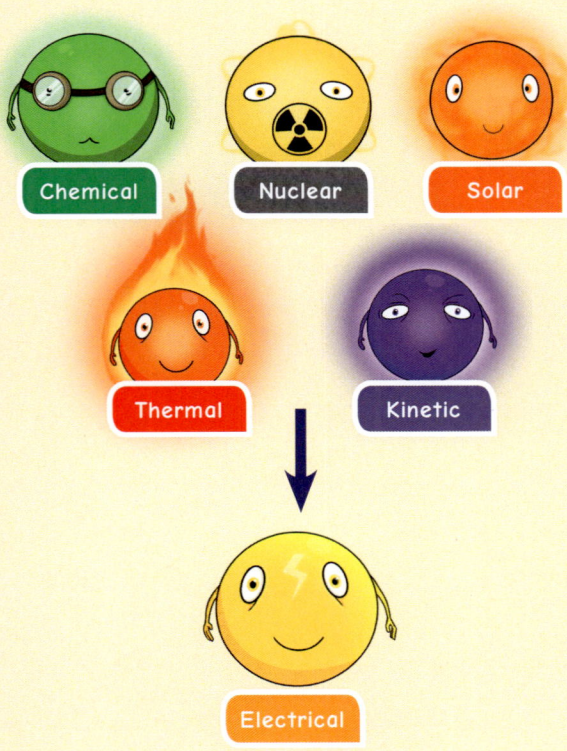

Chemical    Nuclear    Solar

Thermal    Kinetic

Electrical

- **Fossil fuel power stations** cause a lot of **pollution**.

## 32 Low Emission Energy

- Wind, wave and hydroelectric power stations produce very **little** pollution.

Wind

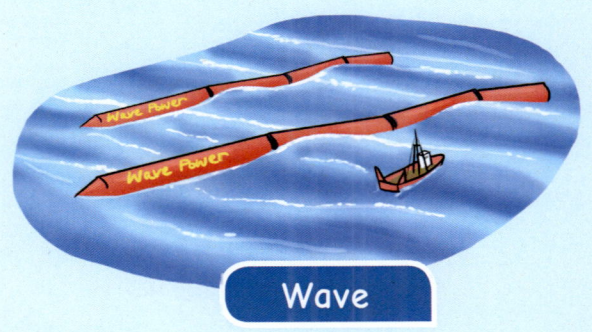

Wave

Hydroelectric

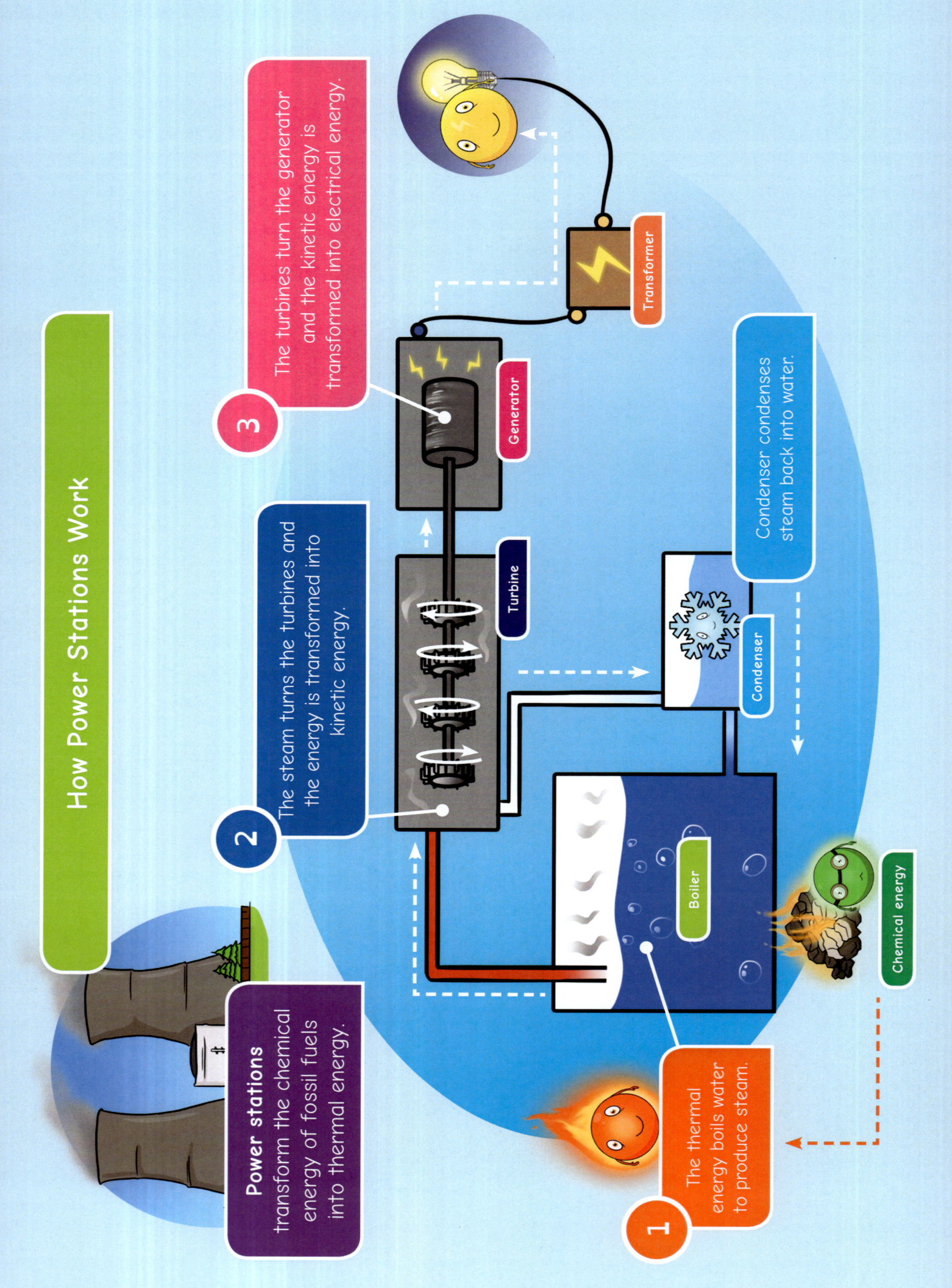

# How Power Stations Work

**Power stations** transform the chemical energy of fossil fuels into thermal energy.

**1** The thermal energy boils water to produce steam.

Chemical energy

Boiler

**2** The steam turns the turbines and the energy is transformed into kinetic energy.

Turbine

Condenser

Condenser condenses steam back into water.

**3** The turbines turn the generator and the kinetic energy is transformed into electrical energy.

Generator

Transformer

# Power & Costs
## KS3 only (Not CE)

## 33 Power is Measured in Watts (W)

- **Power** tells us how much **energy** we are using **each second**.

- **Power** is measured in **watts** (W).

Power is measured in watts (W)

## 34 Workout the power!

The current = 5A

The voltage = 12V

- To work out the **power** in a simple circuit:

power = voltage × current

SO....

12V × 5A = 60W

The power is 60W!

## 35 What Are Joules?

- We measure energy in joules.

- **1 Watt = 1 Joule** of electrical energy **transformed** per second.

- These are very small units!

## 36 How To Measure Energy

- To work out how much we pay for electricity we use kilowatt hours (kWh).

1 kW = 1000 watts

×

1 hour = 3,600 seconds

- If 1,000 Watts are in a kilowatt and 3,600 seconds are in 1 hour. We times these together and this gives us 1 kWh.

=

1 kWh = 3,600,000 j